DATE DUE

5/15/66			
12/18/66			
GAYLORD			PRINTED IN U.S.A.

BASIC BIBLE READER: GRADE THREE

BIBLE
ADVENTURES

by Carol Ferntheil

Illustrated by

Donald Mills

STANDARD PUBLISHING
CINCINNATI, OHIO   2713

FOLLOWING A TRADITION

The new Basic Bible Readers are a beautiful, up-to-date edition of the famous Standard Bible Story Readers, by Lillie A. Faris, that were first printed in 1925. More than a million copies of the earlier editions have been added to the libraries of homes, schools, and churches in the past four decades.

The best of the former readers has been retained in this new series, including the favorite Bible stories that forever appeal to our children. However, all of the illustrations are completely new —drawn by noted children's artists of today.

© MCMLXIII, THE STANDARD PUBLISHING COMPANY
Cincinnati, Ohio   Printed in U.S.A.

Introduction

In the public schools today, the child has practically no contact with the Bible. The home and the Bible school must provide the opportunities and the materials if the child is to learn to read the Bible with pleasure and understanding.

Bible Adventures is the fourth in a series especially designed as supplementary reading for Primary-grade pupils. From the wealth of Bible stories available, each one is selected for the age for which it has a special appeal.

The *third-grade child* reading this book will add to his vocabulary words that he must know in order to read the Bible. The word lists beginning on page 124 make it possible for him to refer to Bible words as he uses the book, just as he learns new words from his public school reader. If he is not at all familiar with Bible words, it would be wise to give him first the Basic Bible Readers, Grade One: *I Read About God's Love* and Grade Two: *I Read About God's Gifts.*

The *parents* may plan family devotions around some of the stories or poems in this book, so that the child can contribute by reading aloud. Stories that are read sometimes from the Bible may at other times be read from this book. Children may be encouraged to follow up Bible-school lessons by reading the stories in their own Basic Bible Readers.

The *Bible-school teacher* will find this book particularly useful in any unit of Bible study. It will be a valuable addition to the reading table. And, if a book is provided for each class member, class time may be used for group reading of stories. When drill is needed for recognizing and understanding certain Bible words, the teacher can choose sentences and pages where that word is used.

The *librarian* will find this a useful book for parents and teachers to borrow as they plan how to tell Bible stories to third graders or as they try to decide which religious books to buy for children. Its library use should not be limited to adults, however. Children who do not own this reader should be allowed to borrow it from the library to read at home.

DEDICATION

This book is lovingly dedicated to those boys and girls who are beginning to read for themselves the wonderful story of God's love.

Stories

Bible Verses

Poems

Also in This Book

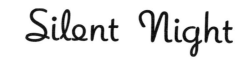

Silent Night

Silent night, holy night!
All is calm, all is bright
Round yon virgin mother and child.
Holy infant, so tender and mild,
Sleep in heavenly peace,
Sleep in heavenly peace.

Silent night, holy night!
Shepherds quake at the sight,

8

Glories stream from heaven afar,
Heavenly hosts sing alleluia:
Christ, the Saviour, is born,
Christ, the Saviour, is born.

Silent night, holy night!
Son of God, love's pure light
Radiant beams from Thy holy face
With the dawn of redeeming grace;
Jesus, Lord, at Thy birth,
Jesus, Lord, at Thy birth.

9

Angels Bring Good News

"It is dark tonight," said one shepherd.

"It is hard to see the sheep," said another shepherd. "We must watch them carefully."

"A fire will keep the wild animals away," said another shepherd.

"But we must be careful that the sheep do not get lost," said the first one.

The shepherds watched through the night on the hills around Bethlehem. The stars came out in the sky. The sheep did not go far away. The hours of darkness went by. The shepherds sat by the fire.

10

Suddenly an angel stood by the shepherds. A bright light shone around them. They were afraid.

The angel said to them: "Fear not: for, behold, I bring you good tidings of great joy.

"Unto you is born this day in the city of David a Saviour, which is Christ the Lord."

Then there were many angels. They were praising God and saying,

"Glory to God in the highest, and on earth peace, good will toward men."

Now it was quiet. It was dark again. The angels were gone.

The shepherds were still on the hillside. They looked around. The sheep were safe. 11

The shepherds were excited. They wanted to find out more about this good news.

"Let us go to Bethlehem," they said. "The town is not far away."

"How will we know the Saviour?" another said.

"By the angel's directions," said one. "He will be wrapped in swaddling clothes, lying in a manger."

They hurried on the way. Bethlehem was not a large town. They soon found the stable. They saw Mary and Joseph with the baby Jesus. He was lying in a manger just as the angel had said.

Then the shepherds left, excited and happy. They had seen the baby Jesus. He was the Saviour. They told everyone they met.

What wonderful news! The angels had told them first! They had seen the baby first! They gave thanks to God for the baby Jesus.

12

The Baby Jesus in Danger

Mary and Joseph knew that the baby Jesus was a very special child. Before the baby was born, God sent angels to tell them about Jesus.

One angel came to Joseph. He brought this message: "Thou shalt call his name Jesus: for he shall save his people from their sins."

13

An angel also came to Mary. He brought the same message: "Thou shalt call his name Jesus. The Lord God shall give unto him the throne of his father David. Of his kingdom there shall be no end."

There were other people who knew that Jesus was a special child. Wise-men in the East saw a special star in the sky. They knew that it meant a special child was born. He would be king of the Jews. They waited to worship Him. They followed the star.

The Wise-men traveled a long way. They came to Jerusalem. They began asking, "Where is the new baby, the king of the Jews? We have seen His star. We have come to worship Him."

Soon King Herod heard about them. Was there a new king? How could there be? After all, Herod was king. He did not want another king around. He had to find out about this king. Then he would make sure the new king could never take his place.

King Herod called the wise men of his own land. "Where was the baby to be born?" he asked.

"In Bethlehem of Judaea," all the wise men answered. "It is written in the book of the prophet."

Then King Herod sent for the Wise-men from the East. "When did you first see the star?" he asked. By their answer, he knew when Jesus had been born. He knew how old the child would be.

"Go to Bethlehem and find Him," King Herod told the Wise-men. "When you find Him, come and tell me. I want to go to Bethlehem to worship Him, too."

The Wise-men went toward Bethlehem. The star went before them. Suddenly the star stopped. It was over the place where Mary and Joseph were living with the young child Jesus. The Wise-men were happy. The star had led them to the baby King. Now the star shone over the house.

The Wise-men went into the house. They saw the young child with Mary, His mother. They worshiped Him. Then they opened their treasures and gave Him rich gifts.

The Wise-men gave Jesus gold and frank-incense and myrrh. These were gifts for a king. The Wise-men rejoiced to find the new king.

But they did not tell Herod about Him. God sent a dream to warn the Wise-men. He told them to go home another way. He did not want them to go back to Herod. The Wise-men went back to their country another way.

God knew that Jesus was in danger. Since the visit of the Wise-men, King Herod was looking for the child. Herod wanted to kill Jesus. He was afraid that Jesus would take his place as king.

God sent an angel in a dream to tell Joseph this message: "Awake, and take the young child and his mother, and go into Egypt."

16

Joseph knew that the child's life was in danger. He got up at night. He awakened Mary and Jesus. They started along the rocky path toward Egypt.

The journey was very dangerous. The rocky path was hard to travel. The desert land had no food. Many thieves were along the way. And Herod's soldiers might find them. The soldiers had orders to kill Jesus.

Mary and Joseph were afraid of the dangers. But they knew that God would take care of Jesus.

As God watched over them, they traveled along the road to Egypt. They stayed there till King Herod died. Then God sent an angel to tell Joseph that it was safe to return home. Jesus was no longer in danger from King Herod.

17

Jesus and the Devil

As Jesus grew up He learned to work for His heavenly Father. He learned the Commandments that God had given to Moses. He talked with God in prayer. He worshiped in the synagogue.

Jesus was God's Son. God had given Him a special work to do on earth. When Jesus was a man, it was time for Him to do His special work on earth. Jesus was to teach people how to live a good life. He was to show them the way to the heavenly home. He was to save people from sin.

Jesus wanted to do everything right. When it was time to begin His work, He went to John the Baptist. He asked to be baptized.

John baptized Jesus in the Jordan River. Then a voice from heaven said, "This is my beloved Son, in whom I am well pleased." Now Jesus was ready to do His work.

But someone wanted to stop Him. The devil did not want Jesus to work on the earth. He did not want people to be good.

Jesus was fasting and praying in the wilderness. He had not had anything to eat for forty days and nights while He prayed. He was very hungry.

The devil came to Jesus. "If you are the Son of God," said the devil, "command these stones to be made into bread."

Jesus could have done this. He was very hungry. But He did not want to take orders from the devil. He did not want to use His power just for himself. He answered, "Man shall not live by bread alone." To obey God is more important.

Next the devil took Him to the highest place on the roof of the temple. "If you are the Son of God," said the devil, "jump down from here. Then people will believe you. They will see that God has sent His angels to care for you."

Jesus answered, "Thou shalt not tempt the Lord thy God." He knew that God's angels would help Him if He were in danger. But He would not ask them to help Him show off. That would be foolish.

Then the devil took Jesus up on a high mountain. They could see all the countries of the world. "All these countries are mine," said the devil. "I can give them to anyone. All these things will I give you, if you will fall down and worship me."

"Get away from me," Jesus told the devil. "I will not worship you. It is written, 'Thou shalt worship the Lord thy God, and him only shalt thou serve.'"

The devil finally left Jesus. He could not get Jesus to do anything wrong. Then God sent angels to take care of Him.

Jesus was ready to do His work on earth. He could show people how to turn away from evil. He could show them how to say no when the devil wants them to do something wrong.

On Guard

(Poem over six hundred years old.)

Guard, my child, thy tongue,
That it speak no wrong;
Let no evil word pass o'er it;
Set the watch of truth before it,
That it speak no wrong:
Guard, my child, thy tongue.

Guard, my child, thine eyes;
Prying is not wise:
Let them look on what is right,
From all evil turn their sight.
Prying is not wise:
Guard, my child, thine eyes.

Guard, my child, thine ear;
Wicked words will sear:
Let no evil word come in,
That may cause thy soul to sin;
Wicked words will sear:
Guard, my child, thine ear.

21

Listening to Jesus

"I wonder why so many people are walking up that mountain!" the boy thought. He was standing by the road, dressed brightly in his red cap and red belt.

"I must see where they are going," he decided. He followed the people.

"Where are you going?" the boy asked a man.

"To see Jesus," the man replied. "Sometimes He goes into the mountains to rest."

"Will I see Him?" the boy asked.

"Oh, yes. He will teach us about God. Sometimes He will heal the sick."

The boy hurried along. A great crowd had gathered around Jesus already. The boy stood in the back. He could see Jesus plainly.

Now he knew why people followed Jesus, even up the mountain. Jesus told them how to live happier lives. He told them how to please God by obeying Him. The boy remembered every word.

Jesus taught them, saying:

"Blessed are the poor in spirit: for theirs is the kingdom of heaven.

"Blessed are they that mourn: for they shall be comforted.

"Blessed are the meek: for they shall inherit the earth.

"Blessed are they which do hunger and thirst after righteousness: for they shall be filled.

"Blessed are the merciful: for they shall obtain mercy.

23

"Blessed are the pure in heart: for they shall see God.

"Blessed are the peacemakers: for they shall be called the children of God."

"Ye are the salt of the earth."

"Ye are the light of the world."

"Let your light so shine before men, that they may see your good works, and glorify your Father which is in heaven."

"Take no thought, saying, What shall we eat? or, What shall we drink? or, Wherewithal shall we be clothed? . . . for your heavenly Father knoweth that ye have need of all these things. But seek ye first the kingdom of God, and his righteousness; and all these things shall be added unto you."

"Ask, and it shall be given you; seek, and ye shall find; knock, and it shall be opened unto you. For every one that asketh receiveth; and he that seeketh findeth; and to him that knocketh it shall be opened."

"All things whatsoever ye would that men should do to you, do ye even so to them: for this is the law and the prophets."

THE BUILDER

Jesus was a good teacher. People would listen to Him all day. They had never before heard a teacher so wise and interesting. Sometimes He would tell stories that would help them understand Him better.

One day the people had listened to Jesus all day as He taught on the mountainside. He wanted to tell them that listening to Him is not enough. They must remember to do the things He said. They must live as He showed them how to live. He told them this story:

A wise man built his house upon a rock. That was hard work. He built a good foundation. He wanted a good house.

A foolish man built his house upon the sand. He did it the easy way. He did not try very hard to build a good house.

Then the storms came. The rain came down until there was a flood. The wind blew hard.

As the storm beat upon the house that was built on the sand, it fell down. The foolish man was like the people who listened to Jesus but did not do what He said.

As the storm beat upon the house that was built on the rock, it stood fast. The storms could not hurt it because it was built well. The wise man was like the people who listened to Jesus and did the things that He said.

Are you a wise person or a foolish person? Do you do the things that Jesus says to do?

The Prodigal Son

A parable is a story that teaches a lesson. One parable that Jesus told is the story of the prodigal son.

The boy in this story was a prodigal son because he did not use money wisely. He did not use any of it for God's work. Here is the story that Jesus told:

A man had two sons. The older son was wise and worked hard for his father. But the younger son was foolish. He said, "Father, give me the part of your money that belongs to me."

The younger son gathered all his things. He went on a trip to a country far away. He spent money for everything he wanted. He made new friends. He paid for their good times.

Soon all his money was gone. He was hungry. He needed new clothes, but he did not have any money. He looked for his new friends, but they did not want to see him if he could not pay for their good times.

He tried to find some work to do, but there were not many ways to make money in that country. Finally a man told him that he could take care of his pigs. The prodigal son had to go out in the field to feed the pigs. He even wished he had some of the scraps that people gave the pigs. He was so hungry. His clothes were in rags.

Now he was sorry that he had been foolish. "My father's servants have enough to eat," he said. "I will go back to my father. I will tell him I am sorry I have done wrong. I will ask him if I can work as one of his servants. Then I will have enough to eat."

The prodigal son walked a long way back to his own country. When he came near his home, his father saw him coming. His father ran to meet him. He threw his arms around him.

The son said, "Father, I have done wrong. I will not ask to be called your son again. Please let me be a servant at your house."

But the father called for fine clothes for his son. He gave him shoes and a ring. He had a feast with his best food. The father said, "I thought my son was dead, but he is alive. He was lost, but now he is found. Let us be merry."

The older son was unhappy. He had worked hard, but there had never been a party for him. His father said, "Son, all that I have is yours. But your brother was lost and is found. It is right that we should be happy."

Do you know what Jesus was trying to teach in this parable? God wants us to do what is right. But when someone does wrong, and then is sorry for it, God is happy to have that person come back to Him.

Jesus Comes to Jerusalem

"Hosanna! Hosanna!"

People were standing all along the road into Jerusalem. They were waiting for Jesus. They wanted to praise Him. They wanted to show Him that they loved Him. They wanted Him to know they were happy to have Him for their Saviour.

"Hosanna! Hosanna!" they called. "Blessed is he that cometh in the name of the Lord."

Jesus knew that the people were waiting for Him. He knew it would be a very special time. He wanted a little donkey to ride.

Jesus sent two of His helpers to a village. He told them where to find a little donkey. He told them to untie it and bring it to Him.

"If anyone tries to stop you," Jésus said, "tell him that the Lord needs this animal."

The two helpers found the donkey. They untied it. Someone said, "Why are you taking the animal?"

Jesus' helpers answered, "The Lord needs him." The men let them go on their way.

The helpers brought the donkey to Jesus. They threw some coats on the animal's back. Then Jesus sat on the donkey's back.

The people of Jerusalem were waiting to see Jesus. They were standing along the road looking for Him. When they saw Jesus coming, they threw their coats on the road to make it softer for Him.

They cut branches from trees. They spread leaves and palms on the road to make it softer. They waved palms as they cried, "Hosanna!"

The people knew that Jesus was the Son of God. They knew that He was the Saviour. They wanted to praise Him. The people of Jerusalem treated Jesus as a king.

Many people had heard Jesus teach about God and His heavenly home. He had made them very happy. He was their friend. As He passed along the road, they kept calling, "Hosanna! Hosanna!" It was a very happy day.

32

Jesus was pleased to hear the people praise Him. He was their friend, and He loved them. He knew He would not be with them much longer. Soon it would be time for Him to go back to His heavenly home to be with God. He would not be a king on earth; He would be their king in heaven.

Jesus hoped that the people would remember the things He had taught. He hoped that they would live in the way He showed them. He wanted them to obey Him so that He could be their Saviour.

Just a few days after this happy time, the wicked people would make Jesus die on the cross. He would die for the sins of all the people. Then He could truly be their Saviour. But the people did not know this sad time would come so soon. They were happy to praise Jesus.

Jesus rode slowly along the road. "Hosanna! Hosanna!" the people cried. The children waved palms. "Blessed is he that cometh in the name of the Lord. Hosanna in the highest!"

33

The Old Rugged Cross

On a hill far away stood an old rugged cross,
The emblem of suffering and shame;
And I love that old cross, where the dearest and
   best
For a world of lost sinners was slain.

O that old rugged cross, so despised by the world,
Has a wondrous attraction for me;
For the dear Lamb of God left His glory above,
To bear it to dark Calvary.

To the old rugged cross I will ever be true,
Its shame and reproach gladly bear;
Then He'll call me some day to my home far away,
Where His glory forever I'll share.

So I'll cherish the old rugged cross,
Till my trophies at last I lay down;
I will cling to the old rugged cross,
And exchange it some day for a crown.

In All the World

Jesus was living again! How happy His friends were! They could see Him and talk with Him.

But Jesus would soon leave them. He spent much time talking to His friends about heaven. He would be living there with His heavenly Father. He would hear their prayers.

Jesus told the eleven apostles how to carry on His work. Then He had them go out to a special mountain. Jesus told them that it was time for Him to go back to heaven.

He gave one last commandment to His apostles and to all who would follow Him. He said:

"All power is given unto me
in heaven and in earth.
Go ye therefore, and teach all nations,
baptizing them in the name of the Father,
and of the Son, and of the Holy Ghost:
Teaching them to observe all things
whatsoever I have commanded you:
and, lo, I am with you alway
even unto the end of the world."

As His friends watched, Jesus was lifted up into heaven.

We still have His commandment today. When we say that we will follow Him, we know that we should tell all the world about Him. How are you helping the children around the world to know about Jesus?

Fairest Lord Jesus

Fairest Lord Jesus,
King of creation;
O Thou of God and man the Son!
Truly I'll love Thee,
Truly I'll serve Thee,
Light of my soul, my joy, my crown.

Fair are the meadows,
Fairer still the woodlands,
Robed in the blooming garb of spring;

Jesus is fairer,
Jesus is purer,
He makes our sorrowing spirits sing.

Fair is the sunshine,
Fairer still the moonlight,
And all the twinkling starry host;
Jesus shines brighter,
Jesus shines purer,
Than all the angels heaven can boast.

—*Silesian Folk Song*

39

Preaching in a Chariot

Jesus had gone back to heaven to live. His helpers were trying to obey His commandment: "Go ye therefore, and teach all nations, baptizing them in the name of the Father, and of the Son, and of the Holy Ghost." Jesus' helpers began to travel through all the world that was known at that time.

Philip was one of Jesus' helpers. Philip traveled first to Samaria. Philip had been given the power to do miracles. He was able to make people well. Big crowds would gather to see what he did. Then he would teach the people about Jesus.

The people listened to Philip. They said, "This man is the great power of God." They listened as Philip preached about Jesus. They came back to hear him again and again. Many of them believed in Jesus and were baptized. Some of the important men in Samaria believed in Jesus because of Philip.

Now he would preach to someone even more important. An angel gave Philip this message from God: "Arise, and go toward the south unto the way that goeth down from Jerusalem unto Gaza."

Philip followed the directions. He was walking along the road when he saw a chariot. The man in the chariot was from Ethiopia. He was a man who had great power. He had charge of all the queen's money.

The man had been to Jerusalem to worship God. Now he was returning home. As the chariot went along, he was reading the book of the prophet Isaiah.

41

Philip ran to the chariot and said, "Do you understand what you are reading?"

The man answered, "How can I, unless someone explains it to me?" Then he invited Philip to ride in the chariot.

The man was reading the part of Isaiah that told about Jesus. It said that Jesus would die for the sins of people. Of course Philip knew all about Jesus. He could tell the man about Jesus' life and Jesus' teaching. Then something very important happened. This is how the Bible tells about it:

"And as they went on their way, they came unto a certain water: and the eunuch said, See, here is water; what doth hinder me to be baptized?

"And Philip said, If thou believest with all thine heart, thou mayest. And he answered and said, I believe that Jesus Christ is the Son of God.

"And he commanded the chariot to stand still: and they went down both into the water, both Philip and the eunuch; and he baptized him.

"And when they were come up out of the water, the Spirit of the Lord caught away Philip, that the eunuch saw him no more: and he went on his way rejoicing" (Acts 8:36-39).

Blinded, But Saved

Far across the sea from Jerusalem there was a city called Tarsus. A little boy grew up there. His name was Saul. He was a Jew.

Tarsus was far away from Jerusalem where most of the leaders and teachers of the Jews were living. When Saul grew older, his father sent him there to study with one of the great teachers.

Saul learned to obey the laws of the Old Testament and to worship God. He also learned about Jesus. But he did not believe in Jesus. He thought that all the people who believed in Jesus were wrong. He thought they should be punished.

One day Saul heard that people were teaching about Jesus in another city. He asked important men to give him letters. These letters said that he could bring the people to prison. Saul and some friends started along the road to the other city. They really hated the Christians.

As Saul and his friends were walking along the road, suddenly everything looked different. A bright light from heaven was shining around Saul. He fell to the ground with surprise and fear. What could be happening? Then he heard a voice.

Speaking in the blinding light, the voice said, "Saul, Saul, why do you work against me?"

"Who are you, Lord?" Saul asked in fear.

"I am Jesus. You are making great trouble for my followers. You are working against me."

Saul was shaking all over. He asked, "Lord, what will you have me do?"

"Arise, and go into the city," Jesus answered. "You will be told what you must do."

Saul stood up to go into the city. He opened his eyes. He turned his head. But he could not see. Saul was blind.

The men who were with Saul could not say a word. They had heard a voice, but they did not see anyone. They did not understand the message Saul had been given by God. But they could tell that Saul was blind. They took him by the hand to lead him into the city.

Saul could not look for the Christians then. He could not see. For three days and nights he did not eat or drink anything.

Saul stayed in his room and thought about what had happened. Why did the bright light blind him? Why did the Lord speak to him? Was he wrong in hurting the people who preached about Jesus? Were the Christians the ones who were right?

Saul had time to think. He began to understand God's message. Then God sent a man to talk with Saul. His name was Ananias.

"Go to a certain house," God told Ananias. "There you will find a man named Saul. Put your hand on him, and he will be able to see again."

45

Now Ananias was afraid. "Saul has done much wrong to the Christians," he said. "He came to this city to put us in jail."

"I have special work for Saul to do," God answered. "He will preach to many people, even to kings."

Ananias did not question God's command.

"Brother Saul," said Ananias, as he went into the house, "the Lord, even Jesus, appeared to you. Now He has sent me to help you receive your sight and to receive the Holy Spirit."

As Ananias said this, Saul could see immediately. He had come to believe in Jesus. Now he was very sure. He was baptized at once. He had been blinded, but his soul had been saved!

After eating, Saul felt stronger. He talked with many of Jesus' friends. He asked questions. He listened to them. Soon he was able to preach.

"Do you see who is preaching?" people said.

"Why, it is the man who came to put the Christians in jail."

"It is the same one who hurt many Christians in Jerusalem."

"Could he be a Christian now?"

They wanted to find out. They listened, and learned about Jesus.

Now the Jews were very angry. "This man came to take the Christians to jail. Now he is helping them," they said.

"Let us hide by the gates of the city," one man said. "He will go out sometime. Then we can kill him."

The Jews took turns waiting. But Saul knew they were there.

Some of Saul's friends took a big basket to the wall of the city. They had a strong rope on the basket. On a dark night Saul climbed into the basket. His friends let it down the wall. Slowly, the basket went down. Finally it reached the ground. Saul was safe. He could go on his way now to teach and preach for Jesus.

47

An Earthquake in Prison

It was a dark, still night in the prison at Philippi. The jailer had fastened the prisoners by their feet. Then he locked the doors and went to bed. The hours passed slowly to midnight. Most of the prisoners tried to sleep.

But there was a sound from the inner room of the prison. The other prisoners could hear men praying. Then the men began singing praises to God. Why would men sing in prison? This was something the other prisoners could not understand.

The prisoners praising God were Paul and Silas. After Saul became a Christian, he was called Paul. His life was changed completely; and his name was changed, too. When his name was Saul, he had put Christians in prison. Now he was a Christian, and he was in prison.

Paul and Silas had not done anything really wrong. They had helped a girl who was sick.

But some men did not like to see Paul and Silas get so much attention. "These men are causing trouble," they said to the rulers in the market place. "They teach us to do things that are wrong."

48

Then the rulers had Paul and Silas beaten and put into prison. Their feet were locked in place. Their backs hurt from the beating.

Still, these Christians could sing praises to God. They could pray for His help. That is what the other prisoners heard. Even though it was midnight, Paul and Silas kept singing and praying to God.

49

Suddenly the prison began to shake. The building was moving. The prisoners were frightened. It was an earthquake!

The walls and floors were moving. The doors came open! The prisoners were free. They could all walk out. But no one did!

The jailer came running. If anyone escaped he would be killed.

Then he heard Paul's voice. "We are all here." No one had left the prison.

The jailer knew that Paul and Silas were not like other prisoners. There was some reason for all these happenings. He fell to his knees before Paul and Silas.

"Sirs," he said, "what must I do to be saved?"

They said, "Believe on the Lord Jesus Christ, and thou shalt be saved, and thy house."

Then Paul and Silas preached to the jailer and his family. They told them about Jesus. They said that they could be saved if they would believe and obey Jesus.

That night the jailer and his family were baptized. The earthquake had frightened them. But it had opened their hearts to the message that Paul and Silas preached. Now they were all Christians.

SHIPWRECK!

Paul was often in danger because of his work for Jesus. He was often put in prison. Most of the time, no one could say that he had really done anything wrong.

Some of the rulers of the land decided to send Paul to Rome. Then he could talk to the ruler of all the land. They found a ship that was sailing toward Rome. Paul was put on the ship. He was a prisoner. Soldiers were sent to guard him.

The ship was very slow. It had to stop at many cities. Soon the good weather would be over. It would not be safe to sail in the winter.

Paul said to the men on the ship, "Sirs, I see that this trip will be full of danger. The ship and the things loaded on it will be in danger. And the lives of men will also be in danger."

But the master of the ship decided to go on. The good weather did not last very long. Soon the wind began to blow. The ship rolled in the waves. The wind blew harder and harder. The ship tossed and turned from side to side.

The men gave up trying to set the sails. They just let the boat drift in the wind. Then they started to throw things off the ship. Now the strong winds had turned into a real storm. The storm went on for days. They could not see the sun in the daytime or the stars at night.

Then Paul stood up and spoke in a loud voice: "You should have listened to me. I told you that this harm would come to you. But be of good cheer, for none of you shall lose his life. God, whom I serve, sent an angel to stand by me.

"The angel said: 'Fear not, Paul. You will be saved because you must be brought to Rome. God has given you the safety of all those who sail with you.'

"Now be of good cheer, Sirs, for I believe that God will do as He says. But the ship will be lost. We will be left on a strange island."

Was Paul right? The sailors wanted to believe him. For two more weeks, the ship tossed in the wind and storm. Then, one dark night about midnight, the sailors put down a rope to see how deep the water was. "We must be near land," they called. They threw out four anchors to try to stay in this place.

They watched for morning. As they waited, Paul spoke to them. "Take some food now," he said. "We have had nothing for two weeks. You will need to be strong. But you will not be hurt."

Then Paul took the bread and gave thanks to God for it. The men felt more cheerful.

It was a long wait through the dark hours. They threw more of the ship's load into the sea. Finally there was enough light so that they could see a strange land. With the wind still blowing and the waves high, they slowly made their way toward shore. There was a bang and a jerk, and they stopped. The ship had run onto some rocks and was struck. The ship began to break apart.

The sailors knew they must leave the ship, even in the middle of the storm. The soldiers who were guarding Paul decided that they should kill him. But the captain of the soldiers knew that Paul somehow had kept them safe. He would not let the soldiers carry out their plan.

The captain ordered everyone who could swim to jump into the water and swim to the land. The others were to hold on to boards and broken pieces of the ship. The waves pushed them toward land. Finally all of them were safe.

The people on the island were kind. They saw how cold and wet the men were. They built a fire and brought food to the men. Paul helped to gather wood. As he put some sticks on the fire, a poison snake came out and bit his hand.

"He will die," the men whispered. "He must have done something wrong. This is to show that

he should die." They watched Paul from a distance. But his hand did not get sore. He did not get sick. Then they knew that he was someone special.

Sick people then came to Paul, and God gave him the power to make them well. For three months they stayed on the island. Paul preached to the people and helped those who were sick. When better weather came, a ship arrived at the island. They were able to continue their trip to Rome.

And so Paul was able to tell many people about Jesus. He was able to take the gospel message to another part of the world.

PSALM 100

Make a joyful noise unto the Lord, all ye lands.

Serve the Lord with gladness: come before his presence with singing.

Know ye that the Lord he is God: it is he that

hath made us, and not we ourselves; we are his people, and the sheep of his pasture.

Enter into his gates with thanksgiving, and into his courts with praise: be thankful unto him, and bless his name.

For the Lord is good; his mercy is everlasting; and his truth endureth to all generations.

57

A Child's Prayer

Lord, teach a little child to pray,
    And O accept my prayer!
Thou hearest ev'ry word I say,
    For Thou art everywhere.

A little sparrow cannot fall,
    Unnoticed, Lord, by Thee;
And though I am so young and small,
    Thou dost take care of me.

Teach me to do whate'er is right,
    And when I sin, forgive;
And make it still my chief delight
    To love Thee while I live.

—Brown

Abraham's Long Journey

Abraham had lived a long time in a good land. He had fine cattle and sheep. He had strong camels. He had good farms to grow food. He had a beautiful wife named Sarah.

One day God spoke to Abraham. "Go out of this country, out of your father's house," God said. "Go to a land that I will show you. I will make of you a great nation. I will bless you and make your name great. And I will bless the people who bless you, and hurt the people who hurt you. Because of you, all the families of the earth will be blessed."

What a wonderful promise this was. Abraham was a good man. He wanted to do exactly as God said. He took his wife and Lot, his brother's son. They got ready for a journey. They took all the people who lived in their household. They took their farm animals. They took their clothes and their jewels. They loaded everything they could take on camels. Many things would be left.

It was hard to leave the land where they had lived a long time. They were really rich people. But they went to the new land that God told them they would have. The land was called Canaan.

When they reached Canaan, God said to Abraham, "To your family will I give this land."

Then Abraham built an altar because God had spoken to him there. Later he named the place Bethel. Bethel seemed to be a good place for a home. Abraham hoped he could stay.

But there was no rain for a long time. The land was very dry. Food would not grow. Abraham could not grow food for all the family and all the cattle, too. He had to journey again. This time he went to Egypt. There was plenty of food in Egypt.

Abraham kept thinking of the nice place he had chosen for his tent near Bethel. When he heard that the bad weather was over, he started on another journey to go back there. He took all his family and all his helpers. He had many cattle. And he was a rich man, with much gold and silver.

Abraham loaded everything on camels again. The men walked all the way. Whenever they stopped, they put up tents to sleep in. Finally they had traveled all the way back to Bethel. There Abraham found the altar he had built. He prayed to God again. He gave thanks for all the riches God had given him.

Abraham had given many cattle to his brother's son, Lot. Through all the long journeys, Lot had been with him. Now they had so many cattle

that there was not room for them all. The men who took care of Lot's cattle began to have trouble with the men who took care of Abraham's cattle.

Abraham was very kind to Lot. In fact, all the cattle and riches that Lot had were given to him by his uncle. But Lot was not very thankful. He liked to have the best land for himself. He was selfish.

Abraham said to Lot, "The men should not fight as they take care of our sheep and cattle. There is enough land for everyone. Let us divide the land. You may take one side; I will take the other side. You choose the land you want."

Lot looked over all the land. He saw the wonderful green plain of the Jordan River. This land always had water, green fields, and good food.

"I choose the plain of the Jordan River," Lot said. Then Lot went to live in the cities of the plain. Many wicked people lived there. There was much sin. They were not good neighbors.

Abraham took his family and moved farther away. God was pleased with Abraham. God said, "Lift up your eyes and look around from the place where you are. Look to the north, the south, the east, the west. I will give to you and to your family forever all the land you see. Now arise, and walk through the land. Walk north and south. Walk east and west. I will give it all to you."

Then Abraham moved his tent again, to a place called Hebron. He built another altar to God. He gave thanks for God's many blessings.

64

Moses and the Burning Bush

Moses was a shepherd in the desert. Perhaps you do not think of him that way. How do you know Moses? As a baby hidden in a basket on the river? As a boy found by the princess and living in the palace? As a great leader walking between the waters of the Red Sea? Or perhaps you always see Moses as he stands on Mount Sinai holding the Ten Commandments in his arms.

Yet there were many, many years when Moses was a shepherd. He did grow up in the palace of Egypt, but he knew that he was not an Egyptian. His people were the Hebrews, Egyptian slaves.

One day Moses saw an Egyptian beating a Hebrew. This made Moses very angry. He killed the Egyptian. Then he had to leave Egypt. He knew that the king would be angry and kill him.

Moses went out into the desert. He was very hot and tired, so he sat down by a well to rest. He helped some girls who came to the well to water their father's sheep. When the girls told their father about Moses' kindness, he gave Moses work as a shepherd.

As Moses was watching the sheep one day, a strange thing happened. He saw a bush that was on fire. But though the bush was in flames, it was not burning up. It was not hurt by the fire.

When Moses walked closer to see why the bush did not burn up, he heard a voice calling, "Moses, Moses." The voice came from the bush!

He answered, "Here am I."

Then the voice called again, "Do not come

closer. Take off your shoes, for the place where you are standing is holy ground. I am the God of your fathers."

Moses was afraid. He hid his face.

Then God spoke again. "I have heard the cries of my people who are in Egypt. I have seen that they are slaves. I know their sorrows. I have decided that I will bring them out of Egypt. I will bring them to the good land of Canaan. It is a rich land, and I will give it to them.

"To do this, I will send you to the king, that you may lead my people out of Egypt."

This was wonderful news. But Moses was just a shepherd in the desert. He was surprised.

"Who am I," he said, "that I should go to the king and lead your people out of Egypt?"

"Certainly I will be with you," God promised. There were many people for Moses to free. But God knew how to help all of them. "Certainly I will be with you," He promised.

God told Moses how to tell the Hebrew people that he was sent from God. Moses was to tell them of God's promise to give them the land of Canaan. He told Moses of things He would do to the Egyptians so that they would let the Hebrews leave Egypt.

Moses was still not certain. "The people will not believe me," he said.

"Throw your staff on the ground," God said. When Moses did this, it turned into a snake.

"Pick it up by the tail," God said. When Moses did this, it turned back into a staff.

"Put your hand in your robe," God said. When Moses did, his hand came out white with a disease. Then God told him to do it again. When Moses did this, his hand was as well as before.

Then Moses said, "I do not speak very well. How can I speak to all the people?"

"I will tell you what you shall say," God promised. "Aaron, your brother, is a fine speaker. You shall tell him what to say."

Moses knew that he must do God's will. He must go back to Egypt and trust God to take care of him. He would be the leader of God's people.

CROSSING THE RED SEA

God's people were nearly out of Egypt. They were in a hurry. They traveled as fast as they could go. They were not running from the king now. He wanted them to go. The people of Egypt had given them jewels and asked them to go.

God's people had been many years in the land of Egypt. Most of the time they had been slaves. They had been badly treated. They had prayed to God that He would take them out of Egypt.

Finally God had sent Moses to lead them. Perhaps some people had not believed Moses at first. But God had let him do miracles to prove that he was from God. Then the people listened to Moses. They listened to his brother, Aaron. They obeyed God.

The king had not listened to Moses at first. He had laughed at the miracles Moses did. He had laughed when Moses told of the troubles that God would send on Egypt.

But the king had not laughed when these things really happened. There were frogs all over the land, and later there were flies. The cattle, horses, sheep, and camels became sick and many died. Hail came down on the land of Egypt, then locusts came and ate everything that was left in the fields after the hail. There were three days of darkness. But even then the king had not let the people go with Moses.

Then, when it was time for God's people to leave, God caused death among the people of Egypt. The oldest son in every home died. But God's people did not die.

As death passed over the land, God's people prepared for their journey. They packed all their things. But because they had been slaves, they did not have very much. They ate a quiet supper and were ready to leave.

As the people of Egypt realized how many had died, they went to God's people and begged them to leave. They gave them jewels and gold and silver. God's people, who had been slaves, now had great riches.

As they left Egypt, God went before them by

day in a pillar of cloud. By night He went in a pillar of fire to give them light. He showed them when to stop and when to travel again.

After they were on the way, the king of Egypt became angry. He was sorry he had let them go. He wanted them to come back. He chose six hundred of his best chariots. He sent his best soldiers. He got his own chariot ready and went after Moses and the people of Israel.

The Egyptians traveled fast. It did not take them long to reach the people who were camped by the sea.

The people of Israel saw the dust and heard the noise of the chariots. They knew the Egyptians were coming. There was no place to go. The waters of the sea were in front of them.

Then the people of Israel said to Moses, "We shall die here in the desert. Why didn't we stay in Egypt?"

But Moses stood before them bravely. "Do not fear," he said. "See what the Lord will do. Today you see the Egyptians, but you will see them no more. The Lord shall fight for you."

Then the angel of God and the cloud that had been leading the people of Israel went behind them. Now it stood between them and the enemy.

The Egyptians could not see what they were doing.

God told Moses to stand by the Red Sea. He was to stretch out his hand over the sea.

Moses held out his hand. God sent a strong east wind, and it blew all night. It divided the waters and made a dry path in the sea. The children of Israel walked on the dry land through the middle of the sea. God held back the water until everyone was safe on the other side.

The Egyptians saw what had happened. They hurried with their horses and chariots so that they could follow the children of Israel. But God would not hold back the waters for them. As they went through the sea, the waters rolled back together. The Egyptians were all drowned. The soldiers and chariots and horses were under the water.

Then the children of Israel knew that God would take care of them, and they worshiped God and believed what Moses said.

GOD SPEAKS
at MOUNT SINAI

God's people were safely across the Red Sea.
The soldiers of Egypt could not reach them. The
king could not make them come back to Egypt.

Now they were in a desert land. There were
no roads. There were no cities. It was called a
wilderness. There were sandy deserts and rocky
mountains. It was hard to travel. They had to go
very slowly. There was nothing to eat except what

74

was with them and what God would send. There was no place to stay except in the tents they had with them.

God showed them where to travel. He led them to the wilderness around Mount Sinai. They put up their tents and camped near the mountain.

God told Moses that He wanted to give the people some commandments. He would speak to Moses before all the people. Everyone was to spend three days getting ready. They were to clean their tents, wash their clothes, cook their food. After three days, they were to gather around Mount Sinai. They were to gather close to the mountain, but they must not touch the mountain.

God himself would come down to the mountain to talk with Moses. The people must realize His power and His might. God wanted them to hear and to see. Then they would be sure that He had given these laws to Moses. They would realize the power of God.

The people followed all the directions that Moses gave them. On the morning of the third day, there was thunder and lightning. A thick cloud covered the mountain. Then there was a loud call on a trumpet.

The people were afraid. They were shaking with fear. They could hardly walk from their tents to Mount Sinai.

Moses led them from the camp to Mount Sinai. The mountain was full of smoke because the Lord had come down upon it in a fire. The whole mountain shook. The trumpet sounded louder and louder.

Then God called Moses up to the top of the mountain. The people stood below, full of fear, because of the smoke and the thunder. They knew that the Lord was on the mountain.

God gave Moses the Ten Commandments and many other rules for His people. Moses was up on the mountain a long time.

After many days passed, the people forgot that thunder and smoke had come from the mountain. They thought something had happened to Moses. They forgot about God.

They said to Aaron, Moses' brother, "Give us gods to follow. Make us gods to show us the way."

Aaron was afraid of the people. He did not want them to be angry with him.

"Bring me your golden earrings," he said.

Aaron melted the gold in a fire. Then He shaped the gold into a calf. "These are the gods

that brought us out of Egypt," the people said.

The people were happy. They built an altar. They had a special feast. They sang and danced around the golden calf. Already they were disobeying the Ten Commandments.

God saw what the people were doing. He was very angry. He wanted to destroy the people all at once.

But Moses prayed for the people. He asked God not to destroy them. He asked God to remember His promises to the people.

Then Moses went down the mountain. He carried the stones on which the Ten Commandments were written.

"What do I hear?" Moses asked. "It sounds like war in the camp. That's strange. No, it is not war. It is singing."

Then Moses came close enough to see. The people were singing and dancing around the golden calf. Now he knew why God was so angry with the people. Moses was angry, too.

He threw down the stones, and the Ten Commandments broke to pieces. He took down the golden calf, and broke it into pieces. He threw the pieces into the fire. Then he made them into fine dust, and put the dust in the drinking water. This made the water taste bad. "Drink it," Moses commanded the people. He made them drink the bitter water.

"Who is on the Lord's side?" Moses called. "If you are on the Lord's side, come and stand by me." Some of the people came and stood by Moses. Others still wanted to worship the golden calf. Moses gave a command to the ones who stood by him. "Kill all those who still want to worship the golden calf," he said.

Moses was very sad. He told the people who were left: "I will go up to God and ask Him to forgive you."

Moses prayed that God would forgive the people. He even said that he would die for the people if God would forgive them. But God said that the people must be punished for their own sins.

Then God told Moses, "Cut two more stones like the first ones. Bring them to Mount Sinai."

The next morning, Moses went up the mountain again. He was there for forty days and nights. God wrote again the same Ten Commandments on the two new stones.

This time, when Moses went down the mountain, everything was quiet. The people were afraid. They did not want to forget God again.

Moses read them all God's words. The people listened to God's commandments. They did not want to sin again.

The Ten Commandments

I am the Lord thy God, which have brought thee out of the land of Egypt . . .

Thou shalt have no other gods before me.

Thou shalt not make unto thee any graven image, or any likeness of any thing that is in heaven above, or that is in the earth beneath, or that is in the water under the earth:

Thou shalt not bow down thyself to them, nor serve them: for I the Lord thy God am a jealous God . . .

Shewing mercy unto thousands of them that love me, and keep my commandments.

Thou shalt not take the name of the Lord thy God in vain; for the Lord will not hold him guiltless that taketh his name in vain.

Remember the sabbath day, to keep it holy.
Six days shalt thou labour, and do all thy work:
But the seventh day is the sabbath of the Lord thy God . . .

For in six days the Lord made heaven and earth, the sea, and all that in them is, and rested the seventh day: wherefore the Lord blessed the sabbath day, and hallowed it.

Honour thy father and thy mother: that thy days may be long upon the land which the Lord thy God giveth thee.

Thou shalt not kill.

Thou shalt not commit adultery.

Thou shalt not steal.

Thou shalt not bear false witness against thy neighbour.

Thou shalt not covet. . . any thing that is thy neighbour's.

The Spies

"Here they come! Here they come!" The shout went through the camp. Moses had sent men to spy in the land of Canaan. Now they were coming back.

The children of Israel stood along the path into their camp. They pointed with surprise.

"Look at the grapes!"

"Are those really grapes?"

"Did you ever see such a large bunch of grapes?"

It took two men to carry one bunch of grapes. There was other fruit, too. All of the fruit was very large and juicy. It was the best ever seen by these people.

"Where did you get it?" the people asked.

"We came into the land of Canaan," the spies replied. "It is a land flowing with milk and honey; and this is the fruit of it.

"But the people are strong that live in the land. They have built walls around the cities. They are great and strong. The people are like giants."

Now the shouting was gone. Everyone was very still. The people were afraid.

Then Caleb spoke. He was one of the spies. "Let us go up at once and take the land. We are well able to overcome it."

"Yes," said Joshua, another spy. "Let us go at once."

All the other spies were shouting and complaining. "We are not able to go up against these people. They are stronger than we. The people in the land are giants. We looked like grasshoppers to them. We looked like grasshoppers to ourselves."

Then all the people cried and complained. There was crying in the camp all night.

"We wish that we had died in the land of Egypt. We wish that we had died in the wilderness. Why did God bring us to this land where these giants will kill us? Why do we not go back to Egypt?"

While others were crying, some of them decided, "Let us choose a captain. With him as our leader, let us return to Egypt."

Then Joshua and Caleb spoke again. "The land that we saw is a good land. If it pleases God, He will give it to us. Do not fear the people of the land. God is with us."

But the people were angry. They were ready to stone the spies, Joshua and Caleb. They were angry with Moses and Aaron.

To stop them, God himself appeared in the tabernacle. He spoke to Moses:

"How long will it be before the people believe all the signs I have given them? Now I will do to them just as they say. They have not put their trust in me. I will let them die in the wilderness.

"For forty days the spies were in the land of Canaan. Now, for forty years the children of Israel shall be in the wilderness. All those who cried and complained shall die in the wilderness. Only those who are now children shall be able to go in and take the land. But Joshua and Caleb shall live."

Soon all the other spies besides Joshua and Caleb had died of a bad sickness in the wilderness. For forty years the people wandered around. As they grew old and died, they were left to be buried in the wilderness. Those who had been children were grown up.

Joshua and Caleb were good leaders, too, just as Moses and Aaron were good leaders.

The Sun Stood Still

Every day messengers came to the king of Jerusalem. They brought the news from other cities. Lately the news was always about Joshua and the children of Israel. The king was worried.

"Joshua has taken Ai," the messenger said.

"Joshua has destroyed Jericho. The great city walls have fallen down."

"Joshua leads the armies of the children of Israel. Their power is very great."

"The great city of Gibeon has made peace with Joshua. Gibeon will not war against Joshua."

The king of Jerusalem sent for four kings from nearby places. "Come up with me, and help me," he said. "Let us war against the people of Gibeon because they have made peace with Joshua."

The five kings and their armies marched to the city of Gibeon. They camped there, ready for war.

The people of Gibeon were afraid. "Come to us quickly, and save us," they said to Joshua. "All the kings from the mountains are gathered to war against us."

Joshua led his armies to Gibeon. God spoke to him, saying, "Fear them not; I have given your enemies into your hand."

Joshua's armies marched all night. The armies of the five kings slept all night. They did not know enemies were near. Suddenly, Joshua's men took them by surprise. They began to fight. The armies of the five kings turned and ran.

As the armies ran, great hailstones began to fall. More enemies were killed by hailstones than had been killed by swords.

Soldiers were scattered everywhere. Joshua was worried. The enemy soldiers could hide behind trees and rocks. When night came, they could gather their armies together again.

Then Joshua spoke to the Lord. After that he commanded, "Sun, stand thou still upon Gibeon; and thou, Moon, in the valley of Ajalon."

The sun obeyed! It stood still and the moon waited, about a whole day, until the war was over.

Then Joshua tells us:

"And there was no day like that before it or after it . . . for the Lord fought for Israel."

The five kings ran away, too. They found a dark cave and hid in it. When Joshua found them, he had his men roll big stones up to the cave and make a prison of it.

As messengers spread the news of the battle of Gibeon, everyone in the new land feared the children of Israel. Joshua defeated thirty-one kings and took their countries. Then the children of Israel rested from fighting. Soon they could make their homes in the new land God had given them.

AN ENEMY WITH A SPEAR

Three thousand men were out looking for one man. King Saul and his army of three thousand strong soldiers were looking for David. They knew where he was, too. Messengers from the wilderness had come to King Saul and told him where David was.

But the three thousand men did not find David. He found them! This is what happened.

David's men were watching for King Saul. They knew that Saul wanted to kill David. Saul did not like for other soldiers to follow David. He did not like to have another brave leader in the land. He thought he would surprise David.

But David had a good plan. "I will go to Saul's camp tonight," he said. "Who will go with me?"

This would be very dangerous. They would be in the middle of the enemy camp. One of the soldiers said, "I will go with you." His name was Abishai.

In the dark that night, David and Abishai walked through the camp. All the soldiers were asleep. Even Saul's guard, Abner, was asleep.

89

David and Abishai walked to the center of the camp. There, in the middle of all his soldiers, was King Saul. His spear was stuck in the ground. His bottle of water was on the ground near him.

"Let us kill him," Abishai whispered.

"We cannot kill him," David answered. "He was chosen by God to be king. If God wants him to die, his day will come to die. I will not lift my hand against him. But let us take his spear and his bottle of water."

Quietly they pulled the spear out of the ground. Quietly they picked up the bottle of water. Then David and Abishai hurried from the camp.

They went up a hill that looked over the camp. David called to King Saul's guard: "Abner!"

Abner awoke. He knew David's voice. David called: "Are you not one of the bravest men in Israel? Why did you not guard the king?"

By that time King Saul was awake. He knew David's voice. "I have sinned," King Saul said. "I will not hurt you again."

Then David called back: "Look! I have your spear. I stood by you, but I did not harm you."

Then Saul asked David to return to his city. But David knew how often Saul did not keep his promises. David went to live in another place.

A VISIT TO KING SOLOMON

The camel caravan moved slowly across the desert. The camels had heavy loads. They were carrying gifts to Jerusalem.

In the caravan rode a queen, the queen of Sheba. She had made up her mind to see King Solomon. She was taking this long, hot, and dusty trip just to see him.

"Can it be true?" she wondered. Stories of Solomon had spread far and wide. "Does he really have such riches as they say? Is he really as wise as they say? I have come with the hardest questions for him to answer. And I have brought him the richest gifts I have. Does he have more riches than I? Who is the God he worships?"

Her large caravan of camels arrived in Jerusalem. The queen of Sheba went to Solomon's beautiful palace. She gave him the fine spices that the camels had carried. She gave him much gold and many rich jewels.

When she talked with Solomon, the queen of Sheba told him all that was in her heart. She found that Solomon was as wise as the people had said. He was wise in every way. Solomon could answer her hardest questions. He could solve problems. He could explain many things clearly.

The queen of Sheba learned about the God who gave Solomon his wisdom. She watched as Solomon went to the temple to worship God.

When the queen of Sheba had seen Solomon's wisdom, and the house that he had built, the food on his table, all of his servants and the rich clothes they wore, and the way Solomon worshiped God in the temple, she said to the king: "It was a true report that I heard in mine own land of thy acts and of thy wisdom. But I believed not the words until I came and mine eyes had seen it; and, behold, the half was not told me. Thy wisdom and riches are even greater than the report.

"Happy are thy men, happy are these thy servants, which stand continually before thee, and that hear thy wisdom. Blessed be the Lord thy God."

Then the queen of Sheba gave King Solomon more gifts: many spices, and gold, and precious stones, and trees with very fine wood. The king used the trees to make pillars for the temple, the house of the Lord. He used the wood also to make harps for the singers.

In return, King Solomon gave the queen all that she wanted from the riches of his country.

Then the queen of Sheba went back to her own country with all her servants and all her gifts. She had heard the wisdom and seen the riches of Solomon.

Besides the riches of his own land, Solomon had many ships. Every three years the ships brought gold, silver, ivory, apes, and peacocks. Solomon sent to Egypt for good chariots and fast horses and fine cloth. He had so much gold that he made many things out of gold. Silver was as common in Jerusalem as stones.

And yet the riches of Solomon were not as great as his wisdom. Proverbs and advice from Solomon are in the Bible, in the books of Proverbs, Ecclesiastes, and Song of Solomon. Everyone can read the wise words of Solomon in the Bible.

PROVERBS

Trust in the Lord with all thine heart; and lean not unto thine own understanding. In all thy ways acknowledge him, and he shall direct thy paths. (3:5, 6)

A wise son maketh a glad father. (10:1)

He that walketh with wise men shall be wise: but a companion of fools shall be destroyed. (13:20)

Righteousness exalteth a nation: but sin is a reproach to any people. (14:34)

Pride goeth before destruction, and an haughty spirit before a fall. (16:18)

He that is slow to anger is better than the mighty. (16:32)

96

A friend loveth at all times. (17:17)

A man that hath friends must shew himself friendly. (18:24)

A good name is rather to be chosen than great riches, and loving favour rather than silver and gold. (22:1)

Train up a child in the way he should go: and when he is old, he will not depart from it. (22:6)

Answer not a fool according to his folly, lest thou also be like unto him. (26:4)

Where there is no talebearer, the strife ceaseth. (26:20)

Boast not thyself of to morrow; for thou knowest not what a day may bring forth. (27:1)

Let another man praise thee, and not thine own mouth. (27:2)

CHARIOT OF FIRE

Elijah was an old prophet. He had worked for God for many years.

Elisha was a younger prophet. He had followed Elijah and helped him.

EliJAH—EliSHA. The names are partly alike, but do you see the difference?

Elijah was a brave prophet. He had talked to many wicked kings. He had warned them to be good and to tell the truth. He told them God's will.

One time a wicked king was looking for Elijah. God helped Elijah hide in the wilderness near a stream. He sent birds to bring food to Elijah.

One time Elijah asked a woman for food. She had only enough for herself and her son, but she gave it to Elijah instead. After that, there was always enough food for all of them. When the woman's little boy died, Elijah asked God to bring him back to life. And He did.

Another time Elijah called all the people together to worship the Lord. The prophets of Baal wanted the people to believe in their god. They tried to get Baal to light the fire on their altar, but nothing happened. When Elijah prayed to

God, He sent fire for the altar. Elijah warned the people that they should serve God.

One time when the people and the king were very evil, Elijah was hiding in a cave. There was a strong wind and an earthquake and a fire. Then, after all that, God spoke to Elijah in a still small voice. God told Elijah to go find Elisha and choose him to be a prophet.

When Elijah found Elisha, he put his cloak around him to show that Elisha would be the next great prophet. After that, Elisha went everywhere with Elijah, helping him with his work.

Elijah knew that the time would soon come for him to go to heaven. Elisha knew, too, that Elijah would soon leave the earth.

God told Elijah to go to the Jordan River. Elijah and Elisha stood on the bank. Elijah took off his cloak, rolled it up, and hit the water with it. The waters rolled apart, and there was a path of dry land. Elijah and Elisha crossed the river. On and on they walked.

Suddenly, there was a rushing noise in the air. A chariot of fire and horses of fire appeared.

Quickly, the chariot went between the two men. A whirlwind caught Elijah up to heaven. Elisha stood alone, watching Elijah disappear into heaven.

Then Elisha looked around. Elijah's cloak was on the ground. He picked it up and walked back to the Jordan River. There he rolled up the cloak as Elijah had done. He hit the water, and the waves rolled back. Elisha was able to walk across on dry land.

After that, Elisha was a great prophet.

100

Joash Is Saved

In the king's palace there was loud weeping and wailing. The king was dead. His children were dead. The king's wicked mother would be the ruler.

In all the noise and sadness, no one saw a woman run to her bedroom with the tiny baby in her arms. The baby was Joash, the king's youngest son. Everyone thought he was dead. But his good aunt had found him and hidden him. She wanted him to live to take his father's place as king.

As soon as she could, his aunt took Joash to the house of the Lord. There he could be cared for by the men who took care of God's house. As Joash grew up, he learned about God. He learned the laws that God had given.

When Joash was seven years old, his aunt and uncle decided that he should be given the king's crown. But the wicked queen must not know.

They made careful plans. Some men would guard the doors of the queen's palace. Others would guard the temple. Another group of soldiers would guard the city gate. The guards had swords and spears. "Do not let the queen in," they were ordered.

All the people gathered around the temple to hear the announcement. Joash came out of the temple. "This is the king's son," the men from the temple said. "He ought to be king. The queen has no right to be our ruler."

They placed a small crown on Joash's head. The people shouted, "God save the king!"

The queen heard the shouting. She pushed past the guard. She saw what had happened. She ran outside the city and was soon killed.

102

Then seven-year-old Joash was really the king. But he was not old enough to rule. His uncle and aunt had to help him until he grew older. Joash continued to love and serve God.

When Joash grew up and ruled as a king, he decided to repair the beautiful temple of the Lord. It was dirty and in need of repairs. Many of the beautiful things had been taken out and put in temples to gods that were not real.

"Collect money in the cities every year," the king ordered. "Put a large box at the door of the temple. We want to start work right away."

The people were happy to give money when they saw that Joash was really going to repair the beautiful temple. They loved the temple, but they did not like to see it look so bad. They brought much money to repair it.

The workmen hammered every day. They sawed and measured and painted.

When the people came to the temple, Joash made sure that they heard God's laws and all the commandments. They had a beautiful place where they could pray.

The little boy who had been saved had become a good king. The people loved him, and he taught them to love God.

The Feast of Tabernacles

The little boy pulled hard on the big tree branch. "Will this do, Father?" he asked.

This family was building a booth on the mountain. Some people made booths on their housetops. Some made booths in the temple courtyard. Others made booths in the streets. These would be their homes for seven days while they had the feast of Tabernacles.

It had been many years since the people had this feast. The people had been scattered because of the evil in the land. Many of them had been slaves in another land.

Now some of them were home. Nehemiah had come back to Jerusalem. He had repaired the wall. The prophet Ezra began to read God's laws. He read all morning from the book of the Law. All the people stood in the street and listened.

The next day he read again. They learned about the feast of Tabernacles. They had not kept the feast for many years. Now it was time.

The children loved the feast of Tabernacles. It was like a camping trip. They liked to live in the little booths and have special food. It was

hard to be quiet during the long hours when Ezra was reading the Law. But they knew that they must be quiet and listen. That was part of the special feast. After the reading, there would be time for play and for food.

Now the people knew God's laws. They listened to the reading of the Law. They said they would not turn away from God again.

WE PLOW THE FIELDS

We plow the fields, and scatter
    The good seed on the land;
But it is fed and watered
    By God's almighty hand.

He sends the snow in winter,
    The warmth to swell the grain,
The breezes and the sunshine,
    And soft, refreshing rain.

He only is the Maker
    Of all things near and far;
He paints the wayside flower,
    He lights the evening star.

The winds and waves obey Him,
    By Him the birds are fed;
Much more to us, His children,
    He gives our daily bread.
                —*Mathias Claudius*

The Handwriting on the Wall

All over the city, people could hear the sound of laughing and singing. The king was having a party.

The king's name was Belshazzar. He was rich and powerful. He had many servants. Among those who served him were some of the children of Israel. They had been sent to Belshazzar's country when their own land was taken.

As Belshazzar's party went on, the king ordered his servants to bring the golden drinking cups. These had been taken from the beautiful temple in Jerusalem. They were special cups for the house of the Lord.

Now the golden cups were filled with a strong drink. Belshazzar's noisy guests began to drink from them and to praise their gods of gold, silver, wood, and stone.

Everyone was having a good time. Suddenly, the king's face had a strange look. He turned pale with fear. He was looking at the wall.

The guests looked, too. Then they were quiet. The noisy party was over; everyone was afraid.

On the wall, the fingers of a man's hand were

writing words. The hand could be seen very clearly, writing the words on the wall.

But what were the words? Everyone could see them, but no one knew what they meant.

The hand stopped and disappeared. The words remained. But no one knew what they said.

The king sent for his wise men. "A rich reward will be given to the one who tells me the meaning of these words," the king promised.

The wise men shook their heads. They looked at the words. They could not tell the meaning.

The queen heard about the handwriting on the wall. She heard that the wise men could not tell the meaning. She had an idea! She hurried to tell it to the king.

"A very wise man lives in this city," said the queen. "His name is Daniel. He was able to tell many things to the king he served. He serves a great God who gives him this wisdom. I think he could tell you the meaning of the words on the wall."

Belshazzar's servants went out and found Daniel. The king said, "I have heard that you serve a great God who makes you wise. Tell me the meaning of this writing. I will give you the rich reward that I promised to my wise men."

Daniel answered: "I will read the words and tell you the meaning."

Daniel looked around. "Why are you drinking from the golden cups? They belong in the temple at Jerusalem. They belong to God in heaven. You are using them to praise your gods of wood and stone. God does not like this."

Then Daniel pointed to the handwriting on the

wall. "These are the words: MENE, MENE, TEKEL, UPHARSIN. And this is the meaning:

"MENE: God has numbered the days of your kingdom, and it is ended.

"TEKEL: God has weighed your good and bad deeds and has found more bad deeds than good ones.

"UPHARSIN: Your kingdom is divided and given to your enemies."

The meaning of the words did not bring happiness to Belshazzar. But he kept his promise of rich rewards. He gave Daniel a new coat to wear. He put a gold chain around Daniel's neck.

Then Belshazzar told all the guests: "Daniel shall be the third ruler in all the kingdom."

But that very night the meaning of the words came true. The enemies of Belshazzar destroyed the city. They killed Belshazzar.

Jonah Runs Away

"I am going to run away," Jonah decided. "God wants me to go to Nineveh. I shall go in the other direction. I am going far away from God."

The fastest way to go far away in those days was on a ship. Jonah went down to the sea.

"Where are you going?" he asked the men on each ship. He did not want to go toward Nineveh. He found a ship going the other way. "Take me with you," Jonah said.

It was time for the ship to sail. Jonah got on the ship. Soon the ship was on its way across the sea.

God sent a great storm on the sea. The winds blew harder and harder; the waves rolled higher. It seemed that the ship would break to pieces.

The sailors took the things loaded on the ship and threw them into the sea. Still the ship tossed in the waves.

The sailors prayed to their gods. Of course no one heard their prayers. The storm was worse.

The shipmaster found Jonah asleep. "Why are you sleeping?" the shipmaster shouted. "Awake! Call on your God. Ask your God to save us!"

But Jonah was running away from God. How could he call on God for help?

The sailors asked, "What is your work? What is your country? Who are you?"

Jonah answered: "I am a Hebrew. I serve the God of heaven, who made the sea and dry land."

Then Jonah said, "Throw me into the sea. Then the sea will be calm."

The sailors did not want to do that, even though Jonah said he had caused the storm. They tried hard to row to land.

There seemed to be nothing else to do. They picked up Jonah and threw him into the sea! At once the storm was gone and the sea was calm.

As the men on the ship watched, a great fish came up to Jonah. It opened its large mouth and swallowed him. God had prepared this fish.

Jonah was inside the fish for three days and three nights. He told God that he was sorry he had tried to run away.

God had the fish swim very close to the dry land and throw Jonah onto the land.

Jonah did go to Nineveh. Because of his message, the wicked people obeyed God.

ESTHER SAVES HER PEOPLE

The king was looking for a queen. He had sent for beautiful young girls to come from all his kingdom. He would choose one to be his queen.

The king did not have trouble choosing. There were many beautiful girls, but Esther was his favorite. Esther would be the queen!

The king put a crown on Esther's head. He had a great feast for Esther. He gave her part of the palace to live in. She had her own servants.

Who was Esther? No one really knew. No one asked. But the king had chosen her to be queen!

From her rooms in the palace, Esther could see her cousin, Mordecai, at the king's gate. Mordecai had taken care of her as if she were his own daughter. He had sent her to the palace when the king was looking for a queen.

Mordecai was one of the children of Israel who had been taken away from Jerusalem. He and Esther were Jews. Now Mordecai was in trouble. Esther did not know this.

The trouble was caused by Haman. He knew how to please the king. The king gave Haman a more important place than all the other princes. All the servants were commanded to bow down to him.

But Mordecai would not bow to Haman. Mordecai worshiped God. He would not bow down to a man.

Every time Haman passed Mordecai, he became more angry. All the honor the king gave him did not make him feel better. He must punish Mordecai.

Haman set up a careful plan. He would pretend to be a good helper.

"O King," said Haman, "there are certain people scattered through your kingdom; their laws are different from our own. They do not obey your laws."

The king was worried.

"Make a law," said Haman. "Say that all these people shall be killed."

"Then you write the law," said the king.

Haman called the writers, and they wrote the law to everyone in the kingdom. The law said that on a certain day all the Jews were to be killed, even women and children. Not one was to live.

116

Special messengers took the writing all over the kingdom. Everyone read the law.

"Why is the king angry with us?" the Jews cried. "We have not done anything wrong!"

Of course the king did not know that Esther was a Jew. She would be killed with the others.

Esther herself did not know about the law until she received a message from Mordecai. "Do not think you will escape," he said. "You must find a way to help us."

Esther was afraid. She was afraid of Haman. She was also afraid of the king. When he wanted to see people, he sent for them.

If anyone came to see the king and he did not hold out his golden scepter, the person would be killed. If he came to see the king and the king held out his golden scepter, then he was pleased to see him.

Esther knew she must be very brave. The king had not sent for her. She might be killed.

"I will go to see the king," she said. "If I die, I die."

After praying for several days, Esther went to the king's court. She was frightened. She stood at one side of the room. But the king saw her. He held out his golden scepter. He promised to give her her wish.

Esther did not tell him about all the trouble. She invited him to a dinner. Haman was invited, too.

The king asked, "What is your wish, Queen Esther?"

"My people and I are to be killed," Esther explained. "Your law says so."

"Who has done this?" the king shouted. Now he was very angry. "Where is he?"

"Haman has made this law," Esther explained.

Now the king was angry with Haman. He sent Haman away to be killed. Then he made a new law. The new law was written. Messengers took the writing to every part of the kingdom. None of the Jews were hurt.

The Jews were very happy, and they were thankful for what Esther had done. Every year they had a great feast to help them remember her. She had saved all her people from death.

AMERICA

My country, 'tis of thee,
Sweet land of liberty,
   Of thee I sing;
Land where my fathers died,
Land of the pilgrims' pride;
From every mountainside
   Let freedom ring.

My native country, thee,
Land of the noble free,
   Thy name I love;

I love thy rocks and rills,
Thy woods and templed hills;
My heart with rapture thrills
  Like that above.

Our fathers' God, to Thee,
Author of liberty,
  To Thee we sing;
Long may our land be bright
With freedom's holy light;
Protect us by Thy might,
  Great God, our King!
       —*S. F. Smith*

121

Praise God

All people that on earth do dwell,
Sing to the Lord with cheerful voice;
Him serve with fear, His praise forth tell;
Come ye before Him and rejoice.

The Lord, ye know, is God indeed:
Without our aid He did us make;
We are His flock, He doth us feed,
And for His sheep He doth us take.

—*William Kethe*

Praise God, from whom all blessings flow;
Praise Him, all creatures here below;
Praise Him above, ye heav'nly host;
Praise Father, Son, and Holy Ghost.

—*Thomas Ken*

New Basic Bible Vocabulary

Standard's Basic Bible Reader, Grade Three: *Bible Adventures,* follows the Basic Bible Reader, Grade Two: *I Read About God's Gifts.* First in the series of five readers is the Basic Bible Primer: *I Learn to Read About Jesus.* The Grade One Reader is *I Read About God's Love.*

Bible Adventures contains a total of 1126 different words. Of this number, 931 are used in public school basic reading texts through grade three, 42 are former new Bible words not yet introduced in secular texts, and 153 are introduced as new Bible words. A new word is considered a Bible word if it is in Scripture quotations or if it is necessary to a Bible story.

8.	. . .	23.	mourn
9.	. . .		meek
10.	. . .		inherit
11.	tidings		righteousness
12.	swaddling		merciful
13.	thou		obtain
	shalt		mercy
	sins	24.	peacemakers
14.	prophet		glorify
15.	rejoiced		Wherewithal
16.	Egypt	25.	foundation
17.	. . .	26.	. . .
18.	synagogue	27.	parable
	Baptist		prodigal
	baptized	28.	. . .
	Jordan	29.	. . .
	beloved	30.	. . .
	devil	31.	. . .
	fasting	32.	palms
	wilderness	33.	. . .
19.	. . .	34.	. . .
20.	tempt	35.	. . .
	thy	36.	apostles
21.	. . .	37.	therefore
22.	heal		nations
	Blessed		Holy
	spirit		observe

124

38. . . .
39. . . .
40. Chariot
    miracles
    Samaria
    Arise
    Gaza
41. Ethiopia
    Isaiah
42. eunuch
    doth
    hinder
    thine
43. Tarsus
    Saul
    Testament
    Christians
44. . . .
45. Ananias
46. soul
47. . . .
48. Earthquake
    Paul
    Silas
49. . . .
50. . . .
51. Rome
52. . . .
53. anchor
54. . . .
55. sore
    gospel
56. Psalm
    presence
57. hath
    courts
    everlasting
    endureth

generations
58. . . .
59. . . .
60. Abraham
61. Lot
    Canaan
62. altar
    Bethel
63. . . .
64. Hebron
65. . . .
66. Sinai
    Egyptian
    Hebrews
    slaves
67. sorrow
68. staff
    disease
    Aaron
69. . . .
70. locust
71. pillar
    Israel
72. . . .
73. . . .
74. . . .
75. . . .
76. . . .
77. . . .
78. . . .
79. . . .
80. thee
    graven
    image
    thyself
    jealous
    Shewing
    vain

125

	guiltless		destruction
81.	sabbath		haughty
	wherefore	97.	according
	Honour		folly
	commit		lest
	adultery		talebearer
	bear		strife
	false	98.	Elisha
	witness		Baal
	covet	99.	. . .
82.	. . .	100.	whirlwind
83.	. . .	101.	Joash
84.	Caleb		wailing
85.	tabernacle	102.	. . .
86.	Ai	103.	. . .
	Gibeon	104.	booth
87.	. . .		courtyard
88.	swords		Nehemiah
	Ajalon		Ezra
	fought	105.	. . .
	defeated	106.	. . .
89.	Spear	107.	. . .
	Abishai	108.	Belshazzar
	Abner	109.	. . .
90.	. . .	110.	. . .
91.	. . .	111.	Mene
92.	Solomon		Tekel
	caravan		Upharsin
	Sheba	112.	Jonah
93.	wisdom		Nineveh
94.	. . .	113.	. . .
95.	ivory	114.	. . .
	peacocks	115.	Esther
	Proverbs		Mordecai
	Ecclesiastes	116.	Haman
96.	acknowledge	117.	. . .
	exalteth	118.	scepter
	reproach		

126

Cumulative Basic Bible Vocabulary

Through Grade Three

The following list includes the words introduced as new Bible words in the Basic Bible Primer, Grade One Reader, Grade Two Reader, and Grade Three Reader. Words now common in public school third-grade readers are omitted.

Aaron	Bethesda	earthquake
Abishai	Bethlehem	Ecclesiastes
Abner	Bible	Egypt
Abraham	blessed	Egyptian
according	blind	Eli
acknowledge	booth	Elijah
Adam	Caleb	Elisha
adultery	Canaan	endureth
Ai	caravan	Esther
Ajalon	cease	Ethiopia
altar	chariot	eunuch
Amen	Christ	Eve
Ananias	Christian	everlasting
anchor	commit	exalteth
Andrew	courts	Ezra
angel	courtyard	false
Anna	covenant	fasting
apostle	covet	flesh
arise	daily	folly
ark	Daniel	forbid
art	David	fought
Baal	debtors	foundation
Baptist	debts	frankincense
baptized	defeated	Galilee
barley	departed	Gaza
bear	destruction	generation
behold	devil	Genesis
beloved	disease	Gibeon
Belshazzar	doth	glorify
Bethel	dove	glory

127

God	Joshua	perfume	spirit
Goliath	Judaea	Peter	staff
gospel	kingdom	Philippi	strife
graven	Lazarus	pillar	swaddling
guiltless	lest	poison	sword
hallowed	lo	preach	synagogue
Haman	locust	presence	tabernacle
Hannah	Lord	presented	talebearer
harp	Lot	prodigal	Tarsus
hath	manger	prophet	Tekel
haughty	manna	Proverbs	temple
heal	mansions	Psalm	tempt
heaven	Martha	rejoiced	temptation
Hebrew	Mary	reproach	Testament
Hebron	Matthew	righteousness	thee
Herod	meek	Rome	therefore
hinder	Mene	sabbath	thine
holy	merciful	Samaria	thou
honour	mercy	Samaritan	thy
hosanna	miracle	Samuel	thyself
image	Miriam	Saul	tidings
inherit	Mordecai	Saviour	token
innkeeper	Moses	scepter	tomb
Isaiah	mourn	shalt	unto
Israel	myrrh	Sheba	Upharsin
ivory	nation	shewing	vain
Jacob	Nazareth	Silas	wailing
James	Nehemiah	Siloam	wherefore
jealous	Nineveh	Simeon	wherewithal
Jericho	Noah	sin	whirlwind
Jerusalem	observe	Sinai	wilderness
Jesus	obtain	slave	wisdom
Jews	palm	slingshot	Wise-men
Joash	parable	Solomon.	witness
John	Paul	sore	worship
Jonah	peace	sorrow	ye
Jordan	peacemakers	soul	Zacchaeus
Joseph	peacocks	spear	

128